The Man With The Microphone In His Ear

Inside the Mind of a Psychiatrist

by
Arthur Smukler, MD

I dedicate this book to Cindy Shortt (my talented, creative, beautiful daughter), whose enthusiasm and help during this project can't be underestimated.

My training as a psychiatrist started when I was two. It was dark and I was standing in a crib screaming my lungs out. No one heard. No one came. No one gave a damn. Not being heard and not being understood has shaped my life.

Twenty-six years later, on July 1, 1969, I entered Philadelphia General Hospital (PGH), an ancient medical fortress located at 34th and Spruce Street, to begin the first day of my three-year psychiatric residency. Residents from Drexel University School of Medicine (back then it was called Hahnemann Medical School), Jefferson Medical College, and The University of Pennsylvania School of Medicine shared the responsibility for treating thousands of inner city, mentally ill patients.

I got off the elevator at the third floor, walked down the dimly lit hallway, and stood frozen staring at the ten-foot-high metal door that led to the locked psychiatric ward. Four years of medical school and a year of medical internship did not prepare me for this moment. Nothing could have prepared me for this moment. Finally, I pushed the entry button.

"Who is it?" a scratchy voice asked through the speaker above my head.

"Art Smukler, one of the new first year psych residents. There's an eight a.m. meeting." What if when she buzzed open the door, I simply turned around and left? I'd find a phone on the first floor and explain my grave mistake to the chief of psychiatry. A friend had mentioned that there might even be an opening in Internal Medicine right here at PGH.

"Okay. Come in and close the door immediately behind you." The door clicked. I sighed and stepped inside.

What struck me first was the gloom; a grayness hung in the air and obfuscated any attempt for color to inject life into the wide hallway lined with offices on both sides. The only visible window was way down at the other end of the hall, maybe a hundred feet away. Were those bars across it? Dust particles swirled and danced in the muted light, little molecules that I was inhaling. Was Schizophrenia contagious? Of course not. Nevertheless, I held my breath for an extra few seconds. My next breath was tinged with the odor of urine.

A skinny, gray-haired man, six feet tall, bald with a week's worth of facial stubble, shuffled towards me -- tiny steps, jerky and lacking any fluidity. His washed-out Temple University sweatshirt was three-sizes too large and his baggy jeans were wet in the crotch. His face was fixed-and-rigid and dribble oozed down one side of his mouth. As he shuffled, his thumb and forefinger on both hands rolled rhythmically against each other. I turned sideways and let the man pass. What was I thinking when I decided to become a psychiatrist?

A tall, stately, latte-colored woman wearing a beige sweater and a knee-length brown skirt, holding a metal chart, stepped out of a doorway and literally blocked my way. Not so hard since I was half plastered against the wall.

"You're Doctor Smukler, Doctor Arthur Smukler," she said with authority. Her hair was pulled back in a tight bun, each strand fully captive.

"Yeah. That's me."

"Fourth office on your right."

"The meeting room?"

She nodded.

"Who are you?" I asked.

She stared me square in the eyes and didn't break eye contact. I didn't either. Finally the woman answered, "Lena, the head nurse."

I unplastered myself from the wall and extended my hand. "Pleased to meet you, Lena."

After a few long seconds, Lena gave me a quizzical look and her hand grasped mine, a warm, firm grasp.

"Is something wrong?" I asked. "Something I'm missing?"

She sighed and pointed down the hall. "Room 304, Doc."

"…Thanks," I said, and had the distinct feeling she wanted to add something, but thought better of it. Was there a secret to all this madness?

As Lena disappeared into the nursing station, an elderly woman with waist-length, disheveled, blond hair with graying roots, approached. She fluttered her eyes provocatively and hissed like a wild cat. Frozen, I nodded hello, and forced myself to keep walking. A few feet further down the hall, a middle-aged man, black-hair greasy and matted, stood against the wall. His arms were folded tightly across his stained, gray T-shirt, his eyes frozen in place, staring at nothing.

As the hair on the back of my neck stood at attention, I walked straight ahead. The schedule called for a full day of orientation before we would take over our new duties.

I entered Room 304. There were two men and a woman already seated around an empty mahogany table.

"Hi," I said.

"I'm Wayne," a man in his late twenties answered. He smoothed down his full beard and held out his hand. "One of the first year residents."

"Art." I shook his hand.

"Hey, Man," the other guy said, smiling hello. His name was Barry. He was clean-shaven, and wore a multicolored shirt and bell-bottom trousers. "This place looks like it never left the nineteenth century. You think they unchain the inmates when the new residents start their rotation?"

I laughed.

"I'm Cathy," the woman said, meeting my eyes and immediately glancing away. Cathy was at least seventy pounds overweight and wore a black turtleneck sweater and a black skirt.

At that moment, the door opened. A man, medium height, about forty, clean-shaven, boyish features, horn-rimmed glasses, and wearing a brown-tweed sport jacket and brown slacks, sauntered in and sat down at the head of the table.

"Hello," he said, opening his briefcase. "I'm Doctor Richard Newman, call me Rich. I'm the Director of the Inpatient unit."

We all shook hands and introduced ourselves. Rich's smile was warm and assured. There was no evidence of anxiety or misgivings. This place didn't seem to scare him at all.

"Obviously this unit needs some major interior decorating, like a stick of dynamite," he said, causing all of us to chuckle and relax a bit, except Cathy. Eyes frozen on her notebook, she jotted something down.

"Unfortunately the funds to make any cosmetic changes won't be available for at least six months, and by then you'll all be back at the Med School's main campus on the seventeenth floor. Which, by the way, is state-of-the-art and very attractive. Not withstanding, I guarantee that you'll learn more here at PGH in the next six months than you ever thought possible. This is a remarkable facility and a wonderful opportunity to see as much interesting psychopathology as can be found anywhere in the world."

No one said a word.

"Ah, my psychoanalytic intuition senses that you doubt me."

We three men laughed again. Cathy's frozen expression never changed as she scribbled something on her pad.

Rich smiled. "The unit here is unique in that it is set up as a patient government unit. The patients actually vote on whether they get passes or other changes in their status. Even discharge."

"How can that be?" Barry asked. "Aren't these people psychotic? I mean, how can they be expected to know what's best for them if they're--"

"Crazy?" Rich asked.

Wayne and I nodded in unison. Cathy sat writing, her jaw tightly clenched. She looked scared to death. Maybe she was the only sane one in the room?

Rich said, "We try to encourage the healthy part of our patient's mind, the part that can make sensible, healthy decisions. Even when someone is ready to be discharged."

We all nodded.

Rich continued. "To me psychosis is fascinating. In schizophrenia, manic-depression, and paranoia, patients often experience auditory hallucinations and beliefs that are not shared by other members of the human race. They hear voices that communicate with them and think they are being followed by aliens. A schizophrenic woman actually believed that she was the Queen of England, and no amount of logical discussion could shake that idea. However, interestingly, no-matter how crazy she was, her sensorium was intact. She paradoxically knew that even though she was the Queen of England she was also Juanita Espinosa. Parts of her mind were perfectly logical and sensible. She knew that she was in a hospital, and she knew the correct date and time. She also knew she lived four blocks from the hospital and that her phone was disconnected because she couldn't pay the bill. It was my job to make the healthy parts of her mind work better; so she could leave here and rebuild her life."

Rich loosened his tie, hung his jacket on the back of his chair and smiled. "We try to make everything here as comfortable and non-medical looking as possible so that patients aren't threatened or intimidated. To that end we don't wear white jackets, but dress somewhat casually, yet professionally."

For the next two and a half hours, Rich described the types of patients we would be treating and the medications that were used to treat them – anti-psychotics, antidepressants, tranquilizers, and a new drug called Lithium Carbonate. He hoped that we'd get approval to use it sometime before December, in less than four months.

Hmm. In one morning, I learned more about the mind than I did in four years of medical school. Dr. Newman's explanations helped me see a rhythm to things, a sense that all wasn't chaos and craziness. Having someone confident and articulate to guide us, made me feel that my instincts to become a psychiatrist might have been right.

After lunch, Stanley Gerber, a second year psychiatric resident who was scheduled to show us how patient charting worked, burst into the conference room. "Jerome, a paranoid schizophrenic, is out of control," he said, standing in the doorway, his eyes darting first at us, then back towards the ward, then back at us again. Stanley's blond hair was disheveled and his blue eyes couldn't find a place to rest. "He was admitted last week after refusing to eat, shower, or leave the house. Before that happened he was walking around with a hunting knife and saying that people were trying to get him. He thinks we're all out to get him and hears voices that curse and call him names. He's on large doses of Thorazine, an anti-psychotic tranquilizer that we use a lot of up here. I need your help." With that last statement, Stanley motioned for us to follow him.

We followed our new leader down the hallway, past the offices (each one dark and small, maybe eight feet by six feet and furnished with a metal desk and two chairs), past the cafeteria (a washed-out green room with eight wooden tables that seated six-to-a-table), and stopped in front of the dayroom. A woman wearing a gray blouse and a long black skirt with red stains on the front, squeezing an orange so hard that the juice squirted all over the floor, smiled and squeezed more juice on the floor. A skinny man with a scraggly beard moved out of our way muttering, "Bullshit, bullshit, bullshit."

The dayroom was a twenty by twenty-foot room, painted the same green color as the cafeteria. It was furnished with two, worn-fabric couches, a dozen assorted wooden chairs, a battered, brown piano, and a TV console on the far wall. An afternoon soap was on with the sound turned off. Stanley took a syringe out of his sports jacket pocket and removed the plastic needle guard. Wayne shook his head and mumbled a not so quiet, "Jesus." Cathy was nowhere to be seen. "This syringe contains two-hundred milligrams of Thorazine," Stanley said, trying to educate us in a pseudo-brave tone. "If we all approach Jerome together, he's less likely to lose control." This strength in numbers didn't seem all that logical to me, but what did I know...

"Why can't the nurse give him a shot?" Barry said, his voice an octave higher.

"Where's Dr. Newman?" Wayne asked.

I was thinking exactly the same thing.

"He's not here," Stanley said. "Believe me, it's really not a big deal. A few months on the unit and you'll understand exactly what I'm doing. It's right out of Psych 101."

We took a few more steps into the dayroom. Jerome, a tall, stocky, black man, was standing in front of the piano glaring at us. He wore a pale-blue work-shirt and beige, corduroy pants. Beads of sweat dripped down his forehead. The room was empty except for Jerome and Stanley's merry band of idiots. A dozen patients stood in the hallway watching us through the glass window. Holding the syringe behind his back, Stanley approached Jerome.

"Jerome. It's me, Doctor Gerber," Stanley said, inching closer and closer to Jerome -- fifteen feet, ten feet, three feet. Stanley moved his hand from behind his back.

"You're not goin' to shove that thing up my ass!" Jerome bellowed, his eyes narrowing. In one smooth motion, he picked up the piano stool and smashed it against the top of the piano. The stool slid halfway across the room leaving him holding two of the legs high above his head.

"Jerome, calm down," Stanley said, quickly backing away, knocking into Wayne, who tripped and almost fell down. "I'm your doctor, Doctor Gerber," Stanley croaked as he kept backing up. Jerome, body covered in sweat, swung the piano legs like propellers over his head. I lowered my head and moved backwards.

"Lying fuck! You're no doctor. Gerber, fuckin' Gerber peas or beans or baby shit or whatever the fuck Gerbers are or whoever the fuck you are. None a you is anything but a lying fuck!" Jerome ran towards us, swinging the piano legs like clubs.

We all scattered, Stanley and Wayne ran into the nursing station, Barry and I ran down the hall towards the patients. Jerome stood in the middle of the dayroom violently swinging the wooden legs, screaming, "Leave me alone. I hear you. I hear what you're trying to do. No Gerber's going to fuck me up the ass!" Standing next to me, the woman who had squeezed orange juice all over the floor stood frozen in place, her eyes shut.

The man who I had seen shuffling down the hall when I first entered the unit stood very still, except for the pill-rolling movements of his thumb and index finger on both hands. His face looked like it was carved in wax.

Three security men dressed in khaki shirts and pants, nightsticks strapped to their belts, strode into the dayroom and surrounded Jerome.

"Fuck you, assholes!" Jerome screamed, staring at the three men, swinging the piano legs faster and faster. "Fuck you! Fuck you! Not me! Fuck you, you pieces of Gerber-shit!" Spit flying, he charged the security man closest to him, who backed away outside the reach of the piano legs. The other two men approached Jerome from his back. Jerome spun around. Before he could cock the piano legs, the first man tackled him, and the other two men grabbed his arms and legs. Jerome screamed like a bull elephant. "No! No! Fuck you! Fuck you!" At that moment Lena, like a powerful lioness, bounded out of the nursing station holding a syringe. She knelt down and injected Jerome in his thigh. They all continued to hold Jerome down on the ground until two aides rolled a gurney into the room and lowered it. The guards and the aides moved Jerome onto the gurney, strapped down his arms and legs, and put another strap across his waist. They raised the gurney and rolled him away.

Minutes later it was as if nothing out of the ordinary had happened. The patients wandered back into the dayroom, some sitting down on the sofas and staring at the television, a few just sitting and staring into space. One picked up a magazine, holding it upside down, and staring fixedly at the pages... Just another average day on the patient government psych unit where every patient has a vote.

Following my fellow first-year residents, I walked back into the consultation room and sat down. We looked at each other and started laughing hysterically.

Minutes later Stanley opened the door, looked at us and shrugged.

"Psych 101?" I said, as we all continued to laugh. Gerber joined in. With Jerome locked away, we could afford to laugh as long as we wanted.

"Gerber, what was that all about?" Barry asked.

"Honest, that never happened before," Gerber said. "I swear. Over the last six months no one ever threatened us, or threatened me. It's the truth."

"Explain again the purpose of all of us following you," I said.

"Containment. Honest, I'm not a death-seeking masochist. Often with paranoid patients, if they know there are limits, it helps them keep their internal controls more in check. When a patient is psychotic and out of touch with reality, having a few visible staff members to set limits can be very helpful. In spite of what just happened, and the fact that Jerome saw us as a threat rather than a calming force, this meltdown is the exception rather than the rule. The ward is really a fine place to learn. An amazing place."

Stanley stretched his neck to the right, then to the left. "We don't have much time, because tomorrow I start my rotation back at the medical center; so let's go over writing orders and charting, both of which are very straightforward." Twenty minutes into Stanley's explanation, it registered in my over-stimulated mind that Cathy was gone. She never did return, at least to our program.

When that first day ended I was hooked. I was exhausted and overwhelmed, but psychiatry was beyond anything I ever imagined. Voices, delusions, the madness that drove people over the edge into insanity were absolutely fascinating. I wanted to be around when we got to discover how to help these people.

* * *

The next day, Jerome Cotton was assigned to MY caseload. Why me? I thought as I sat in the nursing station reading Stanley Gerber's notes.

He was a fifty-year-old man who worked full-time as a cook for the Philadelphia School District, married twenty-seven years to the same woman, and he had a sixteen-year-old son and a twenty-year-old daughter. There were no serious illnesses, no history of prior psychiatric treatment, and no family history of mental illness except for a brother who drank too much.

Lena walked into the nursing station, hair still in a tight bun, and dressed in a black sweater and a gray skirt. She replaced a dozen metal charts on the rack. I smiled hello and a brief flicker of a smile crossed her lips. Lena was a bit odd, but there was something about her that appealed to me. I turned back to the chart.

One week ago Jerome's wife, Victoria, a first grade school teacher, called the police because for five days Jerome had refused to eat, shower or leave the house. He talked about people trying to get him and walked around with an old hunting knife strapped to his belt.

She said Jerome had never, in the twenty years she had known him, been violent or acted this way. She thought the problem might have started four months ago when their son Clyde was picked up for using marijuana and cutting school. Jerome became preoccupied, less communicative, and would sit for long periods of time in their den with the lights off. Victoria begged him to get medical help, but he refused. On one occasion, Jerome screamed at his son, threatening to knock his head off. Victoria reported that that kind of behavior was definitely out of character, because Jerome was always a kind and gentle man.

Mute and paranoid, Jerome was brought to the hospital in an ambulance. He allowed the Emergency Room doctor to do a physical exam and to conduct an extensive workup. The physical exam, blood tests, chest film, skull x-rays, and EEG were all within normal limits. When Stanley first evaluated Jerome, Jerome glared at him with obvious mistrust, mumbling curses under his breath. Stanley's presumptive diagnosis was Schizophrenia, paranoid type.

My supervision session with Dr. Newman wasn't scheduled for two more days. I guess I could call him, but hesitated. Running to Daddy didn't seem appropriate. Remembering how confident Lena had been when Jerome went berserk, I took a deep breath, walked over to where she sat writing in a chart, and sat down next to her.

"Lena, any suggestions about Jerome? I guess I drew the short straw."

"The short straw, huh?" She smiled and then laughed.

"What's so funny?"

"I'll tell you sometime. Maybe when I get to know you better." She took a sip of her tea. "There's always fresh coffee brewing and hot water for tea. Feel free to help yourself. We all pitch in a buck every week."

"Thanks, count me in." I put a dollar in a small metal box and poured myself a cup of coffee.

Lena said, "Chances are Jerome was cheeking his meds."

"Huh?"

"Not swallowing the pills. Paranoid patients are like chipmunks or squirrels. They hold the pills in their cheeks, swallow the water, and as soon as the nurse leaves, they spit the pills out. Paranoid patients don't trust anyone. Jerome probably thought we were trying to poison him and incorporated us into his delusion. It'll take a few days of intramuscular injections of Thorazine for him to come around. I'd recommend giving him lots of space until the meds start to work. Yesterday, Doctor Gerber did exactly what he shouldn't have done."

"You mean when we all cornered him?"

Lena nodded. "He was already too far gone. You corner anyone that paranoid you need a way to keep him from hurting anyone or hurting himself."

"What would you have done?"

"Tried to gently talk him into getting a shot to take away the fear in his heart, and if that failed I would have called security." Lena chuckled. "You boys were a sight to see."

I laughed. "The thought that went through my mind was the Four Stooges. Thank you."

Lena smiled. I picked up the chart, left the nursing station and walked over to Jerome's room. Part of me was petrified, while the other part was immeasurably intrigued.

Dressed in a white hospital gown, Jerome lay face up on his bed, ankles and wrists bound in leather restraints. He hadn't shaved for days and stared straight up at the ceiling. When he saw me he pulled hard against the leather straps, groaning with exertion. A sheen of sweat covered his dark forehead. His eyes held a mixture of pain, fear, and something very primitive.

How was I possibly ever going to treat this man? What do I say?

As I stared into his eyes, my thoughts drifted back to what Lena said about trying to take away the fear in his heart. Jerome scared me, and at the same time he looked so vulnerable.

An old memory drifted into my mind. I was four years old and in a car driving with my parents. It was early in the morning and I remember sitting in the back seat and asking them where we were going. They said we were going to a store to buy electric trains. I wondered why we were going when it was dark and why I was still wearing my pajamas. My father parked the car and we walked to a one-story building and went inside. We entered a large room that had chairs lining two walls. My parents spoke to a woman behind a desk and I played on the floor, a cold linoleum floor -- black and white squares -- pretending I had a train engine in my hand and choo-chooing the train from one end of the floor to the other. When are we getting the trains? I asked. My mother told me that we'd see them in a little while, but didn't look at me.

Sometime later, the door next to the desk where the woman sat opened and two men dressed in white walked towards me. I looked up at my parents. "Where are the trains?" The men grabbed me and wrapped me in a sheet. "Where are the trains?" I screamed, looking for my parents. They weren't there. I was alone, screaming, wrapped in a sheet. I couldn't move. There were no trains. Only the two men. As I screamed, they carried me into a very cold room and tied me to a table. Another man wearing a green mask put something over my face. I couldn't breathe! The man was trying to suffocate me.

The next thing I remembered was waking up, my throat on fire, and a nurse telling me what a brave boy I had been and that I had beautiful eyes. What did beautiful eyes have to do with any of this? Who cared! My mother came in the room and fed me some ice cream. She said how lucky I was to be in such a special hospital and that I could have all the ice cream I wanted. Later I learned that a doctor had taken out my tonsils, whatever tonsils were.

My parents had lied to me and abandoned me. Without explaining a thing, they let the men wrap me in a sheet and tie me to a table. If I were bigger and stronger and older, it wouldn't have happened. There would have been a war!

I looked down at Jerome and for the first time really understood. The poor guy was staring at the ceiling; sweat beading on his forehead. Was being psychotic any different than being little and confused? In both of those states, there were things that were beyond understanding.

"Hello, Mister Cotton," I said, standing at the foot of the bed, holding the metal chart under my arm. "I'm Doctor Smukler. Doctor Gerber was transferred to another hospital and I'm taking over for him. I'm your new psychiatrist." Slowly, I walked towards the head of the bed and stood next to him.

Jerome glanced briefly at me, struggled against the restraints, finally gave up and stared again at the ceiling.

I put my hand on his shoulder for a moment. Yesterday he scared the hell out of me. Now, at this moment, I was still scared, but more than fear was a sense of empathy. "Mister Cotton, I was hoping you could tell me why you're here; so I can try and help you."

Just silence. He continued to look at the ceiling as if I didn't exist.

I pointed to the chart. "Doctor Gerber wrote that you hadn't been doing well for a number of months, something related to your son using drugs and not attending school. Your wife said that his behavior upset you very much. A short time later you started thinking that people were trying to hurt you."

There was no response.

"No one will hurt you here. This is a hospital and I'm a doctor. It's my job to help people."

Jerome's unblinking eyes continued riveted to the ceiling. I looked up. He was staring at a heat register.

"Mr. Cotton, I think you're looking at a heat register, but since it's July the heat isn't on. This hospital is so old they don't have air conditioning. It was built a long time before either of us were born... Are you hearing voices? Maybe voices coming out of the duct?"

Jerome's eyes flickered but stayed focused on the register. Voices were definitely a lot more interesting than my amateurish monologue.

"Mister Cotton, hopefully the medication will start to work and you'll feel better, not so frightened. The medicine, Thorazine, is to help with the voices you might be hearing and the thoughts that everyone is trying to hurt you. Yesterday you were so frightened you became violent. When you feel better, I can take you out of the restraints. That'll help I'm sure. Being tied up can't be easy."

Jerome just stared at the heat register, my words as impressionable as the summer breeze hitting the side of the building. I left his room, went back to the nursing station, and noted on the chart what had transpired.

* * *

The next morning when I walked into Jerome's room, he still lay face-up in bed in full restraints. The restraints would stay on until I wrote the order to have them removed.

"Good morning, Mister Cotton. It's Doctor Smukler, your psychiatrist," (the guy who has no idea what to do next and is afraid he'll never have the guts to take off your restraints). "Remember? I saw you yesterday morning."

"Why do you have me tied up?" Jerome said, moving his body, trying to pull his arms and legs out of the restraints. The tone of his voice was more confused than angry. Whoever invented Thorazine was a genius.

"Three days ago you became violent. You smashed up a piano stool and came running after the staff with the legs. You're in restraints to protect yourself and any other people you might attack. You scared everybody. You're a big guy and in great shape. We had to have three guards come up to the unit and hold you down."

"I don't do things to hurt people. You can ask my wife, Victoria. She'll tell you."

I nodded. "She said before all this started, you were a very gentle man. She said that nothing like this has ever happened before. Not in all the years she's known you."

Jerome nodded.

"Mister Cotton, do you know where you are?"

He looked at me and stretched his head so he could see outside his door. Only the hallway was visible. The ward, a large room with two lines of ten beds was twenty feet further down the hallway. When Jerome became violent he was transferred to this sparse room with only a bed. The theory was that less was better because it was safer. No objects to throw or to use to harm oneself. "It looks like a hospital, an old hospital.

Why am I in a hospital?"

"Why do you think?"

"You said I tried to hurt people?"

"How about before that. Do you remember anything regarding why you're here?"

"An ambulance. I remember that."

"Do you know why the ambulance came and took you here?"

He shook his head. "Where am I? What hospital?"

"I'll tell you, but first can you tell me the date and who you are?"

"The date? July. I know it's July. The summer of 1969."

"Good. That's right. How about who you are?"

"Jerome Cotton."

I nodded and smiled. "You're in PGH psychiatric ward, Philadelphia General Hospital. Your wife became concerned because you weren't eating or showering and you thought people were trying to get you."

"They are doctor. There's no way I can forget that." He struggled against the restraints. "They're still tryin' to get me. Do I have to stay tied up? I'm no criminal. My arms and hands feel numb."

"I can't let you out until I'm sure you won't hurt anyone."

"I never hurt anyone, Doc. I don't do that."

"You don't remember when you smashed the piano stool and were swinging the legs over your head running after us?"

Jerome looked up at the heat vent, then back at me, and shook his head.

"Mister Cotton, the way you're acting, it seems like you're hearing voices.

Jerome just kept staring.

"What are they saying?"

Jerome took a deep breath and licked his lips. "They're goin' to get you. Watch out. They're goin' to get you."

A shiver went up my spine. "Who's saying these things?"

"A man."

"Do you know this man?"

Jerome shook his head.

"What does he look like?"

"Like a man."

"Can you describe him?"

Jerome shook his head.

"Not at all?"

"Just a man."

"Does the man say you should hurt people?"

"No."

"What if he tells you to hurt people like he did three days ago? Then what?"

"What do you mean?"

"I mean what will you do?"

"I don't hurt people. I don't do that." He looked back up at the ceiling. Did I dare release him? Would he go berserk again? Yet, leaving him tied up seemed so inhumane.

"Mister Cotton, you have to help me. I can only untie you if I'm perfectly sure you won't hurt anyone or hurt yourself. That makes sense, doesn't it? The rule is that we have to do everything to keep you safe and keep every other patient in the hospital safe. I don't want anyone to hurt you, and I don't want you to hurt anyone. Including me. I don't want you or me hurt."

"Doc, I won't hurt anyone."

"Is that a promise?"

"Yes, Doc." Jerome looked me square in the face. "I promise."

"What if the voices tell you to do something destructive?"

"Doc, I gave you my promise."

"We still need to give you medicine. Do you promise to cooperate with the staff and not give them a hard time?"

Jerome nodded.

"You sure?"

He nodded again.

"Okay, Jerome. Here's what I think. I'll untie you and we'll take a walk. Then we'll see how you do and whether I need to put the restraints back on. Okay?"

Jerome just kept looking at me, his eyes wide and pleading.

I walked around the bed and unbuckled the first ankle restraint. He moved his leg and I almost jumped backward. Then I unbuckled the second ankle restraint. For a moment I hesitated, my hands lingering above the left wrist restraint. Jerome was fifty pounds heavier than I and was strong, very strong. Shouldn't I get someone from nursing to help me out? Maybe I should call Doctor Newman? I leaned across the bed and unbuckled the left wrist restraint. Jerome flexed his hand and stretched his fingers. Finally, I unbuckled his right wrist and stepped back from the bed.

"Mister Cotton, sit up slowly, and give it a minute before you stand up. You've been flat on your back for three days, and I don't want you to faint from low blood pressure."

Jerome rubbed his wrists; then rubbed his left arm and his right arm. Slowly, he swung his feet off the side of the bed and sat up. Bracing his hands on the mattress, he put his feet on the polished cement floor, waited, and stood up. Even though he was only a few inches taller than me, he was very broad. Jerome would have made a formidable linebacker. Maybe he played football in high school? Slowly, the two of us walked out of the room and headed down the hallway.

When we passed the nursing station Lena stuck her head out. She made eye contact, gave me a wry smile and went back inside. Jerome and I walked to the end of the hall, turned around, and walked back.

"Doc, the voices aren't coming from the duct, they're coming from my ear," Jerome said, as we passed the day room.

"From your ear? Like from inside your head? A voice inside your head?"

"I can't say anymore about it."

"Why?"

Jerome shook his head.

"Did you ever play football in high school Mr. Cotton?" I asked after a few minutes. "You look like a football player."

"Defensive guard," he said, and looked down at the floor. Then he looked up. "Two years at North Philly."

"Are you involved in any sports now?"

Jerome looked back down at the floor and didn't answer. He wasn't acting threatening, but more like he had enough talk for the day. I could relate to that. After three or four slow walks up and down the hallway with Jerome maintaining his silence, I sat down next to him in the dayroom.

"Would you rather stay here or go back to your room?" I asked.

For a moment, he just stared at the TV in silence. Then he said, "Here. I'll stay here."

"Will you be okay?"

He nodded.

With some misgivings, I left him sitting in the dayroom where he blankly stared at a daytime soap, with a guy kissing a very pretty woman.

Back in the nursing station, Lena gave me a big smile, and then turned back to her chart writing. I figured that was about as much affirmation as I was going to get.

For the next week, Jerome was cooperative on the unit and let the nurses give him his injections of Thorazine without any complaints. Everyday, the two of us walked up and down the hallway. He told me how he wanted to go home and how worried he was that he would be fired if he didn't get back to work. I reassured him that they weren't allowed to fire someone who was in a hospital, that there were laws to protect people who got sick. Everyday, I asked about the voices. Everyday, he just ignored the question. No-matter what I said to draw him out, he just avoided the entire topic.

I discussed Jerome's progress with Dr. Newman, and he said for me to be patient; that establishing a good therapeutic relationship was essential and took time. When I inquired how long that might take, he shrugged his shoulders.

One morning as Jerome and I walked down the now familiar hallway, I asked him if he'd like a cup of coffee. He nodded and said he liked cream and two tablespoons of sugar. I got the coffee from the nursing station, and we walked over to the dayroom and sat on a sofa in the corner, away from the other patients.

"You look a little better," I said. "Not as upset and angry." The perpetual scowl and hardness in his eyes were gone. He had a softer look.

Jerome nodded and took a sip of coffee. A slight smile creased his lips.

"Are the voices still there? You know, coming from your ear?"

He nodded. "They come from a microphone."

"Inside your ear?"

He nodded.

"Someone's transmitting through it?"

"I don't know, but whoever it is keeps saying I shouldn't go back to the cafeteria. That's where I work, in the cafeteria at North Philly High. But if I don't go back, I'll be fired."

"What exactly does the voice say?"

"Don't go back. If you go back, they're goin' to fuck you. I don't use bad language, but the voice does. Sometimes it gets real foul."

"Who will fuck you?"

"I don't know, Doc."

"How about we go back in your room and I'll examine your ear. Both ears. In fact, I'll do a complete physical exam."

"You think you'll see it?"

"If I do, you'll be the first to know."

"You know, Doc, you're okay. That other doctor… me and him just didn't hit it off."

I went to the nursing station, got a stethoscope, blood pressure cuff, an otoscope, and a rubber percussion hammer. Back in Jerome's room, I did a careful physical exam, looked with the otoscope in both his ears, tested Jerome's reflexes, and did a complete neurological exam.

"Mister Cotton," I said when I was finished. "You're in excellent physical health. There's no evidence of a microphone planted anywhere in your body."

Jerome nodded and took a deep breath. "Doc, you seem like a smart doctor, but they outsmarted you."

"How?"

"The microphone is real small and you just couldn't see it."

"This otoscope is powerful." I turned on the light and handed it to him. "If it was in there, I'd have seen it."

Jerome just shook his head and handed the otoscope back to me.

"Look, I'm going to get x-rays of the mastoid bones and ear canals and an audiometry test," I said. "The audiometry test is to make sure your hearing's okay. If the microphone's there, it'll show up on the x-rays."

Jerome just nodded. "Do you have to keep giving me those shots? They hurt."

"How can I be sure you'll take the pills. Last time when Doctor Gerber gave you pills, you didn't take them. Then all the trouble started and you became violent."

"I give you my word."

"You'll swallow them when the nurse gives them to you? No funny-business holding them in your cheek?"

Jerome nodded.

I walked to the nursing station and sat down to do the morning charting. Lena sat down beside me. "I saw you and Jerome takin' your morning constitutional," she said, an enigmatic smile playing across her face. "Looks like he's doin' better."

"I think so too," I said, filling her in on my decision to switch over to oral Thorazine.

She nodded and smoothed a stray hair from the side of her face. "Can I ask you a question?"

"Of course."

"Last week when you removed the restraints, weren't you scared of him?"

I thought for a moment and laughed. "When I first met you, you were kind of intimidating. Maybe a little scary--"

Lena broke out in laughter. "I knew you could handle him," she said, laughing even louder.

"You got me assigned to Jerome?"

She nodded, a wide grin plastered across her face. "If you could handle me, you could handle Jerome."

For a moment we locked eyes, and in that moment we became friends. "You're something else," I said laughing.

"Right back at ya," she said, and laughed again.

"Lena, one more question. Why were you so formal or strange or whatever, when we first met?"

"Hmm… Good question. No-matter how many years I've been doing this, I'm also vulnerable to the new resident first day jitters. If we have a good group of residents, life goes pretty well up here. The wrong group can create havoc. When I get nervous, I don't say much, and I get a little controlling."

"A little?"

"You can imagine what my husband has to put up with."

We both laughed.

* * *

A week later, the x-rays and the audiometry test were back. I had been treating Jerome for two and a half weeks and with enthusiasm presented the negative results. I held up the x-rays to the light pointing out how clear the auditory canals were. With my pen, I traced the canals showing how there was absolutely no sign of a microphone. Jerome just shook his head and sighed.

"What? Why are you sighing?"

"Doc, they was just a little too smart for you again. Nothin' against you, but they are very smart."

"Too smart for me?"

"When the doctors weren't lookin' they took the darn microphone out of my ear and just put it right back in when the tests was finished." He smiled. "That's what I mean by smart."

"Mister Cotton, that's not possible. There is no microphone. The voices you hear are feelings that are coming from your own mind. That's why you were brought to a psychiatric hospital, to this hospital. It's my job to deal with microphones and voices." I didn't add that this was my first three weeks on the job and my only experience with microphones was related to the big chrome ones that performers used.

"Doc, you're a smart man. I don't mean you no disrespect, but", he shrugged his shoulders, "the microphone's back in there and sayin' the same things like I told you about."

I took a deep breath. "What things?"

"I told you before. That I should watch out because they're going' to hurt me. They use a lot of bad language."

"Who's going to hurt you?"

"If I knew I'd take care of the problem myself."

"Why do they want to hurt you?"

"I been in the school district a long time and they're afraid of what I know."

"What do you know?"

Jerome looked at me and shook his head. "Doc, I just can't say."

And so it went. No-matter what direction I took, Jerome's island of lunacy never faltered. Every morning we walked and talked. We talked about the Phillies and how Jerome's dream was for the Phillies to win the World Series and to take his family to the ballpark. As the days went by, I looked forward to our discussions. We sipped coffee in the dayroom, talked about sports, hippies, and the war in Viet Nam, but I got absolutely nowhere whenever I brought up the microphone.

The following week, I met with Jerome and Victoria. She was a warm, pleasant woman, almost as tall as Jerome, with dark skin and with a flare for bright colored clothes, a kind of Jamaican look. She never missed her scheduled visits, and according to the nursing report was always the first visitor to arrive and the last to leave. She held Jerome's hand and reiterated what a good man he was and how up until a few months ago he was perfectly healthy. She thought that Jerome was doing much better and thanked me profusely. She also brought up the subject of Clyde, and how their son wanted to visit his father. Jerome shook his head and looked down at the floor. "I can't have him seein' me in a place like this," he said. "I just can't."

I looked around the dingy consultation room, noticed Ted, the patient with the Parkinson's-like shuffle, walking past the partially open door, and sighed. If I had a son, I wouldn't want him visiting me under these conditions. Victoria and I looked at each other, a look that implied that she was thinking the same thing. "What about a day pass this weekend?" I said. "Maybe four or five hours on Sunday afternoon?"

The smile that spread across Jerome's solemn face brought tears to my eyes.

Sunday afternoon, Victoria picked up Jerome at 12 noon and they returned at exactly 5PM.

* * *

The more I got to know Jerome, the more confused I became. From my reading and limited experience, paranoid schizophrenia was described as a global emotional disease, where almost all aspects of a patient's personality were impaired. Jerome wasn't this way at all. His personality was warm and caring and not at all like the patients that were described in the texts by Kraeplin, Bleuler and a half dozen other authorities that I studied. After the Thorazine began to work, Jerome had only two symptoms.

The first was the delusion that there was a microphone in his ear (Delusions are fixed, false beliefs that are unshakeable by logic). The second was an auditory hallucination that voices were talking to him through the heat register, then later through the microphone in his ear (Hallucinations are false perceptions, usually auditory but infrequently visual or olfactory).

When Jerome and I talked about subjects other than the microphone in his ear, he was normal and had a full range of emotions. In essence, unlike a schizophrenic, his personality was intact. He continued to be a whole person, but had an island of psychosis that logic and medication could not touch. The microphone in his ear was not going away.

* * *

Two months after his initial hospitalization, the psychiatric patient government that included all thirty patients, the three resident psychiatrists, Doctor Newman, and a dozen nurses and other staff, voted for Jerome to be discharged. The way it worked was that when a treating psychiatrist recommended discharge, the government usually went along with the recommendation. All governments should work so efficiently. So, Jerome, after a warm thank you and handshake, a prescription for Thorazine in his pocket, and the promise that he would see me as an outpatient, left the hospital with his wife.

Every week, Jerome came to the hospital to see me. After two months he still believed there was a microphone in his ear, but said that the voices were gone. He theorized that the wires from the microphone were cut. In essence, the auditory hallucinations were gone and only the delusion that there was a microphone in his ear remained. I made Jerome promise not to tell anyone but me about the microphone.

Over the next two years, Jerome and I continued to meet. We discussed how important it was for him to spend quality time with his son and wife, and not retaliate if his son showed anger. We spent many sessions discussing how anger was a normal human emotion, and that we all felt it. We worked on appropriate ways to handle anger, various child-rearing practices, and new ways to deal with his boss. Weeks later, Jerome told his boss that the tone he used talking to him in front of the other employees was not kind. The next day, the boss actually apologized to Jerome and said he wouldn't do it again.

Jerome spent time with his son, continued to do well at his job, and came on time for his sessions. The microphone never left his ear and the hallucinations only reoccurred when he was under extreme stress.

On our last psychotherapy visit, before I moved to California to finish my residency, I told Jerome, "Remember, don't tell anyone except your next psychiatrist about the microphone."

He nodded, firmly grasped my hand, and said, "I'm goin' to miss you, Doc. You helped me a lot. You helped my whole family."

"I'm going to miss you too, Mister Cotton. I'll never forget our work together."

As we shook hands, our eyes filled with tears. I realized that it didn't really matter whether Jerome had a microphone in his ear, his nose, or anywhere else. What was important was that the quality of his life was improved and he was a really good person. I helped him become a healthier person and he helped me become a better psychiatrist. I learned numerous things, but what I remembered most was the day I approached him in full restraints. When I was able to recapture the memory and the feelings of when I was placed in full restraints (wrapped in a sheet), I knew what to say and how to help Jerome, because I really understood what he was going through. It is a wonderful example of what is called, "Listening with the Third Ear" -- using our memories and feelings to get beneath the surface and truly understand what someone's trying to say.

Jerome's initial diagnosis of schizophrenia was an error because the pervasive personality flaws usually present in schizophrenia were absent. Jerome was able to relate warmly to his wife and children, able to hold a job, take appropriate responsibility for his behavior, and was able to connect emotionally to people outside of his family. He was a man who did quite well in most aspects of his life, except when it came to dealing with that tiny microphone. Why he developed the problem was probably a combination of stress regarding his son's problems, stress at work, and an underlying biological predisposition to paranoid thinking. Jerome's final diagnosis was paranoia, today known as a Paranoid Delusional Disorder. Researchers currently believe that there is probably no overlap between Paranoid Schizophrenia and Paranoid Delusional Disorder; they are two distinct entities. The etiology is unknown.

The DSM-IV (Diagnostic Statistical Manual) defines the core feature of delusional disorder as persistent non-bizarre delusions (for at least one month) with no indication of schizophrenia or a mood disorder. With delusional thinking the patient interprets his life experiences to fit the delusion. For example: even though the x-rays of Jerome's ear were normal, Jerome interpreted the results to mean that the people who put the microphone in his ear had secretly taken the microphone out right before the x-rays were taken.

Paranoid ideas are explained by a psychological defense mechanism called projection. We still don't know exactly how projection works, but we do know that there is an underlying biochemical/genetic abnormality in the brain that allows it to happen. Just as a movie projector beams a picture across a room, a paranoid patient beams his feelings into another person. Feelings that the patient finds unacceptable are attributed to others. Jerome isn't angry with his boss for not giving him a promotion. In Jerome's mind, the boss and other unidentifiable people are angry with him. Jerome is convinced of this because the microphone in his ear is transmitting bad words, words that criticize him, angry words that he's sure are not coming from him. This mechanism of projection takes Jerome off the psychological hook. He isn't angry; other people are angry. The fact that he ran around the dayroom trying to smash people with two heavy piano legs is conveniently repressed or forgotten.

Neurotransmitters in Jerome's brain functioned abnormally and created an environment where auditory hallucinations and paranoid delusions could exist. We still don't fully understand how this occurs, but a prevalent theory is that it's caused by a genetic flaw. It is similar to diabetes, where a genetic flaw creates a situation where the pancreas can't produce enough insulin resulting in an unstable blood sugar.

In most of us, projection doesn't turn into paranoid thinking. A person might project his feelings and think that people are looking at the pimple on his nose, but he doesn't hear voices talking about his pimple. It's a matter of degree. Jerome crossed the line into overt psychosis and lost contact with reality. The auditory hallucinations (the voices), and delusional thinking (the microphone in his ear) are evidence of a psychotic state. Logic and rational discussion were useless in combating Jerome's psychosis. They are useless in any psychosis.

Thorazine, a vintage antipsychotic medication, removed Jerome's auditory hallucinations, but was unable to remove the delusion. Though I haven't seen or heard from Jerome in decades, I expect that the microphone is still alive and well. If Jerome stopped his medication, there is the possibility that he may have needed re-hospitalization. Even if Jerome continued seeing a psychiatrist and was placed on one of the newer atypical antipsychotic medications, he would still have his little microphone. As good as the new medications are, and they are very good, even they cannot cure a pure delusional disorder.

Fortunately, delusional disorders are rare. In thirty years, I have treated only four. Since people who have delusional disorders often don't come to psychiatrists, there may be a lot more of them out there than we know. How about your neighbor, Tony, the guy you've seen three or four times a week for fifteen years? He takes the kids to Sunday school, mows the grass, and goes to the movies with his family. Then one day, he wakes up and shoots his wife, his three children, and himself. When the police question you, you say what a nice guy Tony was and how you're absolutely shocked. There is every reason you should be shocked. If Tony had a paranoid delusional disorder, there would be no way for anyone to know, unless Tony talked about it. Chances are he didn't talk about it. A part of him knew that if he mentioned how the aliens were going to capture and torture his family, people would scoff.

Tony knew, deep down in his gut, that he was perfectly sane. He knew, that by shooting his family before the spaceship landed, he would save them from torture and pain.

SOME NOTES FROM THE AUTHOR

The Man With A Microphone In His Ear portrays what it was like for a clueless, first-year, psychiatric resident to treat a violent, paranoid man in the early 1970s. It's all true, except that The Man With The Microphone In His Ear is a combination of two patients that I treated during this era. Everything else is accurate, as much as one can expect when writing something decades after the fact.

In 1835, "Old Blockley" was a combination of four buildings -- a poorhouse, a hospital, an orphanage, and an insane asylum. It was renamed PGH (Philadelphia General Hospital) in 1919. In the 1950s it was used as a city public hospital and a nursing home for the indigent. The hospital was closed in 1977. Today the site is occupied by part of Children's Hospital of Philadelphia, the University of Pennsylvania Health System and the Veterans Health Administration.

The cover picture is The State Hospital in Scranton, Pennsylvania

ABOUT THE AUTHOR

Dr. Art Smukler is a psychiatrist in private practice and on the teaching faculty at UCLA. He has won the coveted Golden Ear Award for teaching senior psychiatric residents and the Award For Distinguished Writing at The Santa Barbara Writers Conference. *Chasing Backwards*, a psychological murder mystery, is his first work of fiction. He also has released *Skin Dance*, a mystery.

Printed in Great Britain
by Amazon.co.uk, Ltd.,
Marston Gate.